Keep The Joys of Christmas
in your heart all year Long.

Best Wishes

Grandma Mary + Barbara

A Note to Parents, Teachers, Religious Personnel, and Counselors

This book is designed as a teaching tool to help children ages 4-8 learn values, character traits, and work ethics. In the back of the book you can find the following helpful materials:

- Activities
- Vocabulary
- Lesson Plans
- Lesson objectives
- National Career Development Guidelines

Suggestions for using this book:

- Read the lesson plans, objectives, and career guidelines to get an understanding of what your children should learn from this book.
- Before reading the book to the children, go over the vocabulary and definitions.
- Write any pertinent material on the blackboard.
- Read the book once or twice to the children.
- Do one or more activities after you read the book.

Dr. Mary's Grandma Mary and Bonbon Series

Book 3

Bonbon's Special Christmas

by Doctor Mary Ellen Erickson

Illustrations by Julie Haberman

Building Values, Character, and Work Ethic Books
ISBN number: 978-0-9765453-4-7
Library of Congress number: TX6-076-431

"I'm so excited about Christmas," said Bonbon. "We drew names in school today, and I got Jane's name."

"That's nice," said Grandma Mary as she continued making her cookies.

"I will be getting a gift from someone in school," said Bonbon. "I will also be getting a gift at church, from Santa, and from all my aunts and uncles."

"Hold on there, Missy!" said Grandma. "Christmas is not about getting gifts."

"What will Santa do if he can't bring me gifts?" Bonbon pouted.

"Christmas isn't about Santa Claus either. Christmas is about someone's birthday. Do you remember whom?" asked Grandma.

"Yes. It's Jesus' birthday. I learned that in Sunday School," Bonbon said proudly.

"I am happy you remembered whose birthday it is," Grandma Mary said with a smile.

"There is a legend that says all the animals can speak on Christmas Eve just before midnight," said Grandma Mary. "Maybe they talked to Jesus on his birthday?"

"Maybe they did," said Bonbon as she tried to imagine Jesus talking to the animals.

Grandma Mary made a suggestion. "I think it is time we have an old-fashioned Christmas. You can learn about our family traditions. That way you will learn the true meaning of Christmas. You can start right now by helping me make cookies."

"Is making cookies a tradition?" asked Bonbon.

"It is in our family," Grandma replied. "A Christmas tradition is something you do every year, like a story you tell every year. Baking cookies is a special treat I make for people who come to visit at Christmas time."

"I like this tradition," Bonbon said as she sat down at the table to help decorate the cookies Grandma had baked.

Just then the doorbell rang.

"That must be the postman. "Will you get the door, Bonbon?" Grandma asked.

Bonbon ran to the door, and the postman handed her a whole bunch of cards.

"Look at all the cards you got!" Bonbon exclaimed. "Why do people send cards at Christmas time?"

"Sending Christmas cards is a tradition started in Great Britain around 1840. Most of the early cards showed religious pictures and messages, but now all kinds of scenes are shown on cards with all kinds of greetings."

"Do you like to get cards?" asked Bonbon.

"Yes, I do," Grandma answered.

"Why don't I get any cards?" asked Bonbon.

"Maybe it's because you don't send any!"

"May I send some this year?" Bonbon asked.

"Sure. I'll get you some cards, and you can address them to your friends and relatives," Grandma said as she hurried to get some cards.

Bonbon sat for a long time addressing cards. She was hoping someone would send her a card back.

Early the next morning Grandma Mary and Bonbon drove out to Aunt Doris and Uncle Bud's farm. They were going to get a small, evergreen tree to decorate for Christmas.

"Why do we decorate an evergreen tree for Christmas?" asked Bonbon. "We could decorate a cactus instead."

Grandma Mary laughed. "The decoration of a fir tree is an old German tradition. The evergreen is always green, so some say it represents eternal life. That is why the evergreen is used at Christmas time. This tradition has been carried on for generations in our country."

When Grandma and Bonbon arrived at the farm, Aunt Doris and Uncle Bud came out of the house to greet them. They gave hugs and kisses to Bonbon and Grandma Mary.

After the greetings were done, Uncle Bud said to Bonbon, "Let's go and find the prettiest tree in my field."

Bud took Bonbon's hand, and they walked toward the field where the trees were planted.

Grandma Mary followed.

Aunt Doris stayed home to make some hot cocoa and sandwiches for lunch when they returned.

"Look!" Bonbon pointed.
"There is the biggest, prettiest evergreen
in the field."

"That one is too big for our house!" said
Grandma Mary. "Pick a smaller one."

"How about that one?" Bonbon asked, pointing
to the smallest tree in the field.

"That one will do," said Grandma. "Please cut it
down for us, Uncle Bud."

Uncle Bud hurried and cut down the tree
because it was cold outside. Bonbon waited patiently.

After lunch, Grandma and Bonbon put on their coats and prepared to leave.

"Thanks for the lunch and the tree," Grandma said to Bud and Doris. "I owe you a roast turkey dinner."

"We will be at your house to collect our dinner on Christmas Day!" said Doris.

"Have fun decorating the tree!" Uncle Bud called as Grandma and Bonbon got into the car and drove away.

"Why do we put lights on a tree?" Bonbon
asked as they strung the bright lights on the evergreen.

"It is said that Martin Luther, the Protestant
reformer, was the first to put candles on a tree. He got
the idea from seeing snow glittering on outdoor trees.
People have been decorating trees with candles and
lights ever since."

"Oh," said Bonbon. "I like this tradition, too."

The next day after school, Grandma informed Bonbon that they would be caroling with a group of townspeople. The group would be singing traditional Christmas songs to the elderly and shut-ins around town.

"Who started this tradition?" Bonbon asked as the group walked from house to house.

An older man in the group explained the Christmas caroling tradition to Bonbon. "Many centuries ago a man from Italy by the name of St. Francis of Assisi thought it would be a good idea to sing praises to Christ on Christmas. People started going from door to door singing carols. The people in the houses would give the carolers food, drinks, or money because they thought it would be bad luck if they did not treat the singers."

"I hope we get some cookies and cocoa," Bonbon said.

"We will," the old man answered. "When we are done, we are going to my house for a treat."

"Good!" Bonbon said. "Then I'll keep on singing."

The old man laughed.

The carolers sang with spirit. Bonbon barked
once in a while when she got tired of singing.

On Christmas Eve, Bonbon and Grandma walked to church. It was a lovely, crisp evening.

"Is going to church on Christmas Eve a tradition?" Bonbon asked.

"Yes," Grandma answered. "It is the most wonderful Christmas tradition of all. We go to hear the Christmas story and sing praises for Jesus' birth."

There was much excitement as the children prepared for their Christmas program. Everyone was getting dressed into costumes.

Bonbon was an angel.

The Christmas story was read by the older Sunday school students. The younger children came down the aisle of the church and made a beautiful manger scene.

An older girl read Luke 2: 1-16.

She started reading: *And it came to pass in those days, that there went out a decree from Caesar Augustus, that all the world should be taxed . . . . . .*

When the girl got to the last line, she read: *And they came with haste, and found Mary, and Joseph, and the babe lying in a manger.*

Next, an older boy read Matthew 2: 1-14.

He started reading: *Now when Jesus was born in Bethlehem of Judea in the days of Herod the king, behold, there came wise men from the east to Jerusalem . . . . . .*

When the boy got to the last line, he read: *When he arose, he took the young child and his mother by night, and departed into Egypt.*

Bonbon listened to every word. It was a wonderful story.

After the Christmas story was read, the younger children sang songs. The wise men sang, "*We Three Kings of Orient Are*," and the shepherds sang, "*While Shepherds Watched Their Flocks at Night*."

Then it was time for the three angels to sing. Bonbon was afraid, but the other two angels took her arm and led her up to the microphone. With the help of her friends, Bonbon sang with gusto: "*Angels We Have Heard on High*."

When the program was over, Bonbon and Grandma walked home. Bonbon proudly carried the bag full of goodies she had gotten from the church for being in the Christmas program.

Bonbon awoke on Christmas morning. She was excited. She ran down the stairs to see what Santa had left for her.

"Come and see what Santa brought me!" Bonbon shouted excitedly to Grandma who was in the kitchen working.

Bonbon got a new doll, a book, and a beautiful pair of ice skates.

Grandma Mary opened her gifts. She got a warm sweater, some jewelry, and a new teapot.

"I love Santa!" Bonbon said.

"Did you know that the name Santa Claus comes from a real person?" Grandma asked Bonbon.

Before Bonbon could answer, Grandma went on to explain. "St. Nicholas was a European Christian leader who loved children and gave them gifts at Christmas. Santa Claus is still carrying out the tradition started by St. Nicholas."

After Grandma Mary and Bonbon got home from attending church that morning, people started coming for Christmas Day. Grandma's children and grandchildren came. Aunt Doris and Uncle Bud came.

Everyone brought food to add to the turkey, ham, and mashed potatoes that Grandma Mary was making.

Everyone talked, told stories, laughed, and wished everyone else a Merry Christmas.

It was a very fun and festive occasion.

Bonbon whispered into Uncle Bud's ear, "This is a family tradition because we do it every year."

"Yes, it is, honey," Uncle Bud answered. Then he rubbed his tummy and said, "Having a feast with the family is my favorite Christmas tradition."

Everyone laughed.

After saying grace, the family ate a wonderful Christmas dinner.

Everyone except Grandma Mary, Aunt Doris, and Uncle Bud went ice skating on the city pond after dinner. It was a family custom to go skating if the weather permitted.

"I love skating," said Cousin Becky.

"So do I," said Cousin James. "I'm going to be a hockey player some day when I get big. Playing sports is good for you. It makes you grow strong and healthy."

"I like sports, too," said Cousin Becky, "but I would rather be the coach so I can tell the team what to do."

"That is just like you, Becky," said James. "You like to tell everyone what to do."

Everyone laughed.

"I want to work in a church and put on Christmas programs," Bonbon said. "I liked being an angel."

Bonbon stood up and flapped her arms, pretending she was an angel.

Everyone laughed.

That evening after everyone had gone home, Bonbon played with her doll. She was very sad.

"Why are you sad?" asked Grandma Mary.

"I'm happy we had a special Christmas, but I'm sad it is over," Bonbon replied.

"Don't be sad," Grandma said.

"Remember the lessons you learned during this time of year," Grandma Mary told Bonbon, "and keep the joys of Christmas in your heart all year long."

VOCABULARY

TRADITION: The practice of passing down ideas, customs, and beliefs from one generation to the next.

LEGEND: A story that has been handed down from earlier times.

ETERNAL: Continuing forever: God is eternal.

ORIENT: The countries of Asia, China and Japan are part of the Orient.

CUSTOM: Something people do that is widely accepted. Customs become traditions.

JOYS OF CHRISTMAS: Things we do at Christmas that make us happy.

FESTIVE OCCASION: Joyous or happy event.

CHRISTMAS STORY: St. Luke: 2: verses 1-16 and St. Matthew 2: verses 1-14. Can be found in the BIBLE (King James Version)

LESSON OBJECTIVES

1. Help students to realize the importance of a good attitude.
2. Help students realize the importance of traditional activities.
3. Help students understand that different jobs are done in different environments.
4. Help students get a better understanding of the Christian traditions of Christmas.
5. Help students make good decisions concerning moral development.

NATIONAL CAREER DEVELOPMENT GUIDELINES

I.   Knowledge of the importance of self-concept.
Demonstrate a positive attitude about self and society.
Describe how behavior influences the feelings and actions of others.

VI   Skills to understand an use career information.
Identify the working conditions of recreational and religious occupations.

VII.   Awareness of how work relates to the needs and functions of society.
Describe ways in which work can overcome social problems.

IX.   Understanding how to make decisions.
Demonstrate the importance of good decision-making.
Describe how personal beliefs and attitudes affect decision-making.

Page 25

SING ALONG ACTIVITY

Singing makes people happy. Teaching people how to sing is a very important job. Some letters were taken out of words in the Christmas songs listed below. Use the five letters that are circled and discover the answer to the question at the bottom of the page.

1. ◯ingle Bells
2. Deck the H___lls with Boughs of Holly
3. Oh, Little Town of B◯thlehem
4. Joy to the ___orld
5. Hark the Herald Angels ◯ing
6. Away in a ___anger
7. The Little Dr◯mmer Boy
8. Silent ___ight
9. The ___welve Days of Christmas
10. The Fir◯t Noel
11. Angels We Have ___eard on High

Who's birthday do we celebrate at Christmas? Put the circled letters in the grid below to find out.

___ ___ ___ ___ ___

HOLIDAY FOODS ACTIVITY

Each holiday food is fun to make or eat. It takes a good cook to prepare a good holiday meal. Each holiday food fits into one spot in the grid. Count the number of letters in each word on the list at the left and place the word in the correct spot on the grid below.

★

Cookies	___ ___ ___ ___ ___ ___ (6)
Apple	___ ___ ___ ___ ___ ___ ___ ___ ___ ___ ___ (11)
Potatoes	___ ___ ___ ___ ___ (5)
Fruit Cakes	___ ___ ___ ___ (4)
Turkey	___ ___ ___ (3)
Candy Cane	___ ___ ___ ___ ___ ___ ___ ___ ___ (10)
Pie	___ ___ ___ ___ ___ ___ ___ (7)
Cranberries	___ ___ ___ ___ ___ ___ ___ ___ (8)
Duck	___ ___ ___ ___ ___ ___ ___ ___ ___ (9)

What word does the down ★ grid spell? ___ ___ ___ ___ ___ ___ ___ ___ ___
If you do not know what this word means, look it up in the vocabulary

LESSON PLAN

USE FOR INDIVIDUALS OR GROUPS.

TITLE: Grandma Mary & Bonbon Series: Bonbon's Special Christmas

GRADE LEVEL: K, 1, 2, 3.

SUBJECT AREAS: 1. Personal/Social Development
2. Self-knowledge
3. Moral Development
4. Career Awareness

TIME: 30 Minutes.

MATERIALS: For Individuals: book, copy of activities, pencil.
For Groups: book (overhead copies of each page), pencils, and enough activities for each child.

PROCEDURE:
1. Introduction: "How many of you have family traditions? How many of you know what your family traditions are? Do you know why family traditions are important in developing good values to live by? Today we will learn the answers to these three questions."
2. Read and discuss the vocabulary on page 25.
3. Read the book. Do an overhead for a large group.
4. Ask students the following questions when you are done reading:
   A. What did Bonbon think was the most important activity at Christmas?
   B. Why do we celebrate Christmas?
   C. What Christmas traditions did Grandma Mary teach Bonbon?
   D. What are some of your family traditions?
   E. What are your favorite Christmas traditions?
   F. Why are family traditions important in building good values for us to live by?
   G. What types of jobs (careers) were discussed in the book?
   H. How can we keep the "Joys of Christmas" in our hearts all year long?
5. Hand out the activities. Explain them. Do them.

Look for more Grandma Mary and Bonbon books

First Day of School

Snowstorm

Friendship

In a Pickle

Building a Rainbow

ADHD: A Special Friend